The use of too ⟨...⟩
avoided, as it is ⟨...⟩
encourage comr ⟨...⟩
to expect particu ⟨...⟩

Care has been taken to retain sufficient
realism in the illustrations and subject
matter to enable a young child to have fun
identifying objects, creatures and
situations.

This book belongs to:

ruth

to make the fullest use
of these **Ladybird
talkabout** books.

Ladybird Books Loughborough

compiled by Margaret Keen

illustrated by Harry Wingfield

The publishers wish to acknowledge the assistance of
the nursery school advisers who helped with the
preparation of this book.

talkabout
bedtime

Animals, birds, grown-ups, children:
they **all** need to have **sleep.**

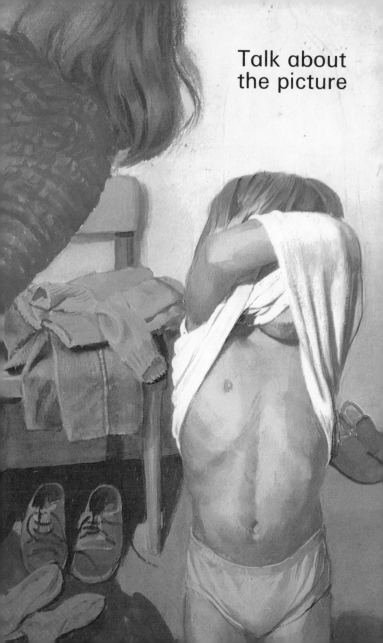

Talk about
the picture

Talk about
getting ready for bed

Which go

ogether?

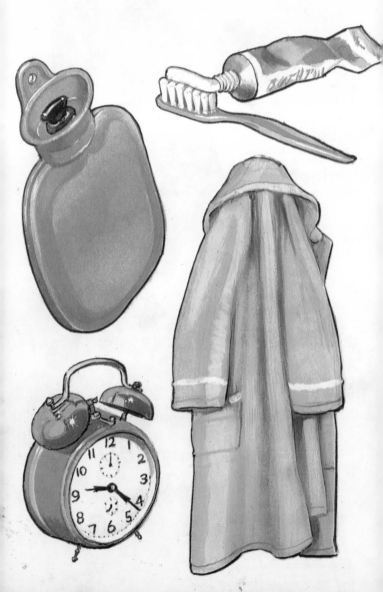

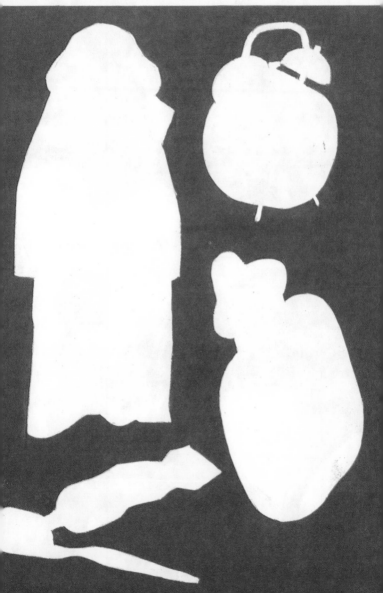

Which would you

take to bed?

Long ago a bad fairy
put a wicked
spell on a
baby princess
so that . . .

. . . when she was
grown up, and pricked
her finger one day . . .

she fell asleep for
a hundred years,

and so did everyone else
in the castle !

Sleeping Beauty

A grown-up could expand it into the full story

Then one day a prince came to the castle.

He found the princess and woke her up with a kiss.

Then everybody else awoke, and the prince married the princess.

Bedtime story

1

2

Talk about noises at night

They work while we sleep

What do they do?

3 lights on

2 lights on

5 lights on

How many
lights are on
in this house?

Wee Willie Winkie
runs through the town

Upstairs, downstairs
In his nightgown.

Tapping at the window,
Crying through the lock,

"Are all those children
in their beds?

It's past eight o'clock!"

Have you seen
any of these beds?

There were 5 in the bed
and the little one said, "Roll over."
So they all rolled over and one fell out.

There were 4 in the bed
and the little one said, "Roll over."
So they all rolled over and one fell out.

There were 3 in the bed
and the little one said, "Roll over."
So they all rolled over and one fell out.

There were 2 in the bed
and the little one said, "Roll over."
So they all rolled over and one fell out.

There was 1 in the bed
and the little one said,
"I've got the bed all to myself."

How many children are in bed?

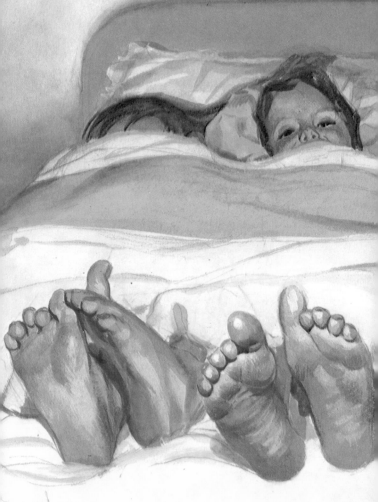

How many feet?   How many

airs of feet?   (A **pair** means **two**)

How many are asleep?

How does
the cockerel
wake them up?

"Let's go to bed," said Sleepyhead.

"Let's sit awhile," said Slow.

"Put on the pan," said Greedy Nan,

"Let's have supper before we go !"

Here are some
animals that sleep
under the ground

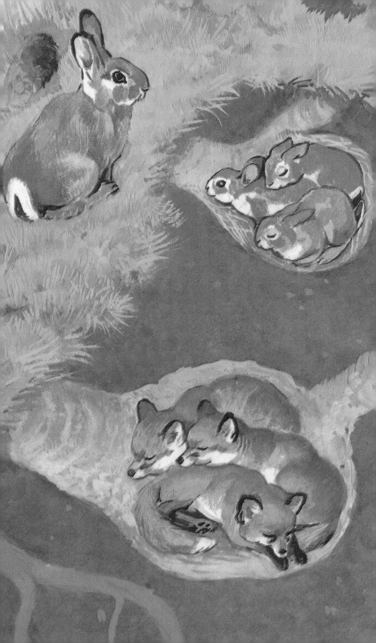

. . and going to bed in a ship

Talk about sleeping in a tent

These wake up
at night
when we go
to sleep

Tell the story

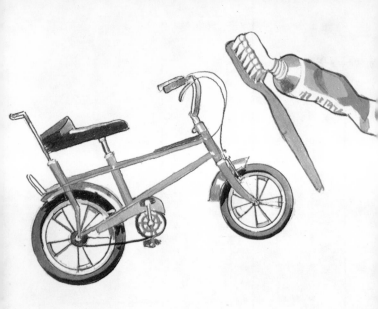

Now look through this book

nd find these again

Suggestions for extending the use of this **talkabout** book . . .

The pictures and page headings in this book are intended as starting points for conversations to help increase a child's vocabulary and understanding. Bedtime is a very important part of a child's day, a time when parents can foster an even closer relationship with a child. Some children readily go to bed after a happy and active day; others can be reluctant and need encouragement and reassurance. All will enjoy looking at and talking about these illustrations. Pages 4 and 5, for example, help a child to realise that every human being and animal must sleep at some time, and pages 6 and 7 will help to reassure him or her that even when alone in bed the rest of the family can be near. Discussion about the picture 'Noises at night' can also give comfort to a nervous child.

The bedtime routine illustrations provide